CAPE VERDEAN

COLORING BOOK

RON BARBOZA

BARIKA PHOTOGRAPHY & PRODUCTIONS

New Bedford, Massachusetts 1995

Acknowledgements

Without the assistance of many, this book would not have been possible. I would, therefore, like to thank all those who have contributed, either directly or indirectly. First, a very special thanks goes to my loving wife, Helen for her love, support, patience, advice and understanding. Next, I would like to thank my children: Ronald Richard Barboza, Jr., Barika Lillian Barboza, Bianca Christina Barboza, and Adia Kendra Barboza for their support and diligent patience.

My father, Anthony Canto Barboza, provided me with constant support, inspiration and advice. Several of my brothers provided me with a fresh way of looking at new options,and some valuable advice. My brothers, Anthony and Kenneth, assisted me in the area of layout design, while Steven helped with some editorial corrections.

I would also like to dedicate this book series to my mother; Lillian (Barros) Barboza, who passed away in 1974. I know she would be pleased with this series. Her guidance, direction and love are always with me.

Additional thanks go to: my paternal grandparents-Antonio Canto Barboza, from the island of Fogo, and Maria Santos Barboza, from the island of Brava, my maternal grandparents-Joseph John Barros and Emily Barros, both from island of Brava, engendered in me a love of Cape Verde.

I would like to extend a special thank you to Alcides Da Graca and his students for their valuable assistance: Vicky DeJesus, Eugenia Da Silva, Dominique Medina, Adelcia Rodrigues, Diva Duarte, Denise Neves, Katia Da Silva, Admir Da Silva, Jose Coelho, Maria Rodrigues, Anis Rodrigues, Eurico Varela, John Duarte, Orfeu DePina, Jailson Lopes, Jair Da Silva, Benjamin Figueiredo, and Levinha Miranda. Mr. Da Graca's insight was essential in accomplishing these two books. I am indebted to him for his kind help.

A sincere thank you to Estyn Williams and Catherine Hassey. Estyn for her assistance with the computer and PageMaker (5.0), and Ms. Hassey for her help in editing. Their assistance was instrumental in completing these books on time.

Additional thanks go to each of the following individuals for their generous assistance in bringing this book to fruition: Mary S.Barros, Jeronimo Barros, Patrica Abu-Raya, Celso Ferreira, Catherine Hassey, Margaret Dias, Diane Carns, Diane Mahan, Richard Legault, Brian Sullivan, Americo Araujo, Dorothy Lopes, Michelle Rosa, Dorothy Lopes, Gail Snow, Donna Romano, and Kenneth Soares. In the event that I have inadvertently forgotten someone, I would like to express my apology for the oversight.

Forward

I have tried to design not only two coloring books, but books that could serve as an introduction to the language of Cape Verdean Crioulo. These books were aimed at being original and unique not only for these two reasons. Each book holds a different chronology that pertains only to the book it appears in. There is a chronology of Cape Verdean History in one book and a chronology of Cape Verdean-American History in the companion book.

It is my sincere hope that these books will be utitlized by both children and adults as an educational tool in bringing a better understanding about Cape Verdeans and their culture. In addition, others may wish to obtain this collection simply for its artistic value. Whatever the reason, it is my wish that the culture of Cape Verde and the Cape Verdean-American Experience will be embraced and shared.

My first visions of Cape Verde came from my four grandparents, who were all born on the islands of Cape Verde. Each came to America onboard a packetship between the "Great Wave of Cape Verdean Immigration". They came from the two neighboring islands of Brava and Fogo between 1899-1919. Their affection and warm recollections of their homeland kept a flame alive in my heart.

Little did I know that these childhood memories would shape my life and future so profoundly. At this stage in my life, I have visited this tiny archipelago off the coast of West Africa a total of seven times. I have countless photographs of the islands, which ninety five per cent of drawings are based upon. The remaining percentage were drawn from archival photographs.

The language of Cape Verde is pretty much an unwritten language that varies from island to island. Therefore, I felt a need to select one dialect for consistency. I have decided to choose Brava Crioulo because three of my grandparents were born on that island. Many of the key words that were used in these books are pronounced the same in all the islands, with slight variations.

In some small way, I hope these books will spread the culture of the people of Cape Verde all over the globe.

Ron Barboza

Cape Verdean History

Chronology

11th Century-Moors travel to Sal (unverifed)
1460 Portuguese official date of discovery of Cape Verde
1462-Diogo Afonso discovers the islands in the Barlavento group
1462-First settlement in Ribeira Grande (Cidade Velha) is established
1483-French sailors reach CVI
1497-Vasco da Gama stops at the CVI
1498-Columbus stops in Cape Verde
1533-Riberia Grande, gains the status of city with a bishop of the Catholic Church
1542-French raid CVI
1576-CVI becomes province of Portugal
1578-Sir Francis Drake raids CVI
1580-1640-Portugal is ruled by the Spanish crown.
1585-Sir Francis Drake attacks Santiago in November
1598-Dutch raid CVI-especially Maio.
1650-1879-Guinea-Bissau was administered from CV
1655-Dutch sacked the town of Sao Filipe, Fogo Island
1699-Willam Dampier's New Voyage stopped at Maio
1774-drought-22,000 died
1817-First public elementary school was established in CV in Praia.
1826-Nova Sintra given the status of vila
1831-33-Drought 12,000 died
1836-Portuguese officiallly abolish slavery
1839-British East India Co. installed coaling stations in Mindelo, Sao Vicente
        -Voyage of the Beagle-Charles Darwin
1842-First printing press in CV, the Tip grafia Nacional.
1851-British Royal Mail Co. installed coaling station
1863-65-Drought 30,000 died
1866-Seminary established in Sao Nicolau
1875-Volcanic eruption on Fogo
1885-Roberto Duarte Silva from Santo Antao was awarded the French Legion of Honor
1900-Drought begins and last for three years-16,000 die
1902-04-drought & famine 15,000 died
1907-Baltazar Lopes da Silva, author, born on Sao Nicolau
1920-1922-drought-17,000 died
1924-Birth of Amilcar Cabral & Aritides Maria Pereira
1933-Pedro Cardosa from Fogo Island publishes "Folclore Caboverdiano"
1936-Claridade-CV literature begins
1940-41-Great Famine -over 30,000 died
1947-Baltazar Lopes da Silva novel Chinquinho about immigration was published
1952-Volcano errupts on Fogo
1956-PAIGC formed
1973-The leader of the PAIGCV, Amilcar Cabral was assassinated
1975-Republic of Cape Verde on July 5 becomes independent
        -Aristides Maria Pereira, becomes Republic of Cape Verdes' first President
        -Pedro Verona Rodrigues Pires, becomes Republic of Cape Verdes' first Prime Minister
1981-CV Friendship American tour
1981-Creation of PAICV
1982-Hurricane Beryl sweeps across Brava
1987-TACV inaugural flight from Boston to Sal
1991-Antonio Monteiro Mascarenhas of MPD was elected President
1991-Carlos Whanon Veiga of the MPD was elected Prime Minister
1992-Cape Verde elected to the United Nations Security Council
        -Cape Verde enters its first world's Fair-EXPO-92 Sevilla, Spain
1995-Volcanic erruption on Fogo Island
        -Republic of Cape Verde participates in the Smithsonian's American Folklife Festival

CAPE VERDEAN

—— *CVC* ——

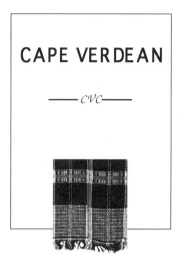

CAPE VERDE ISLANDS
(REPUBLIC OF CAPE VERDE)

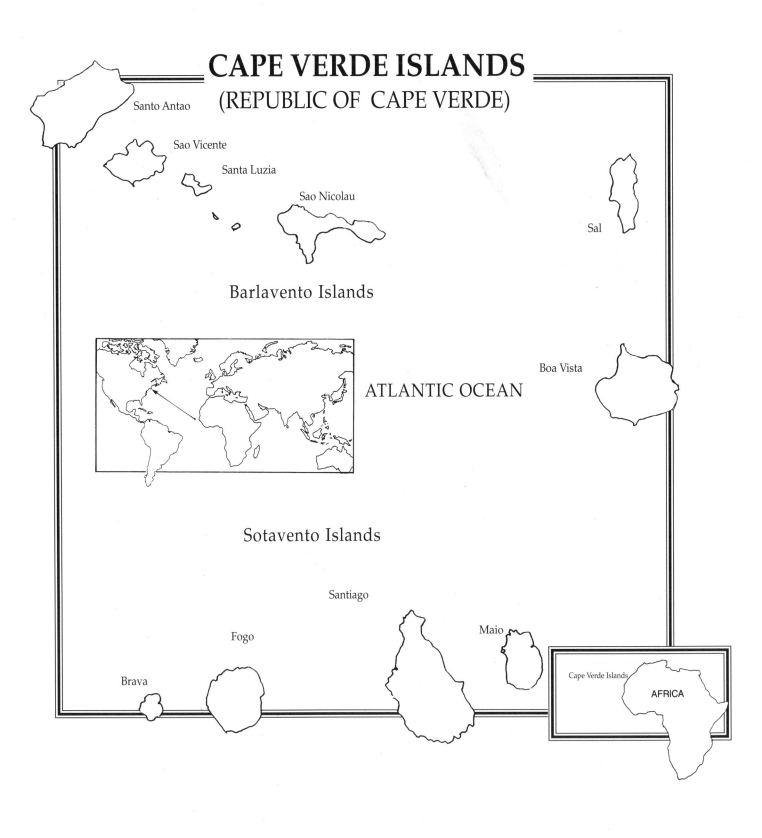

Santo Antao

Sao Vicente

Santa Luzia

Sao Nicolau

Sal

Barlavento Islands

ATLANTIC OCEAN

Boa Vista

Sotavento Islands

Santiago

Maio

Fogo

Brava

Cape Verde Islands

AFRICA

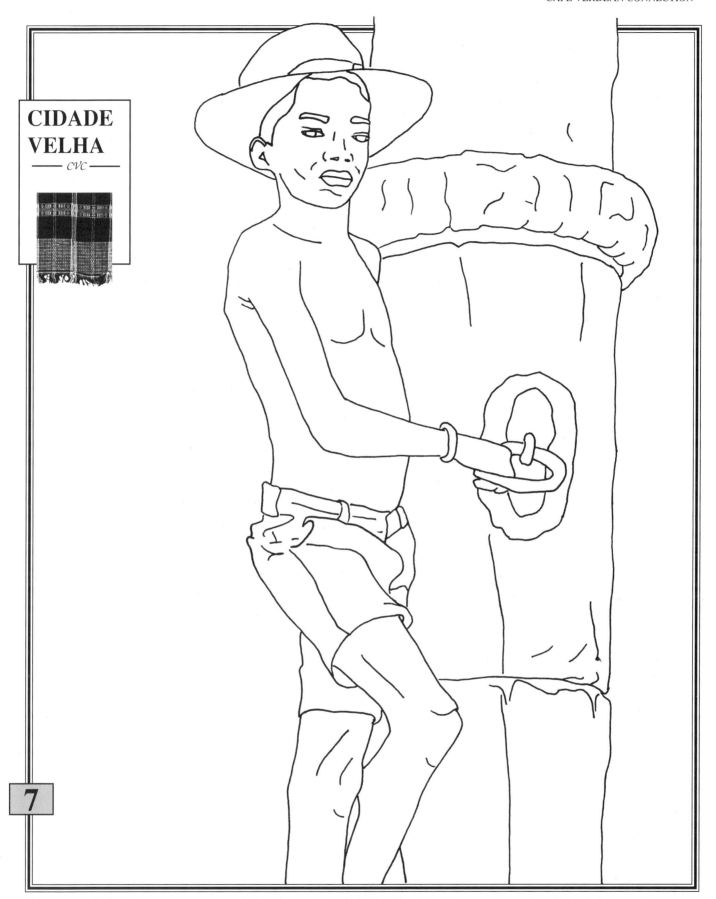

CIDADE VELHA
— *CVC* —

7

Cidade Velha, means old city. In **Cidade Velha,** stands this historic monument to a past, that must not be forgotten. This slave post, doubled as an auction platform for slaves and a place for public punishment.

MERCADO

— *cvc* —

Mercado, means outdoor marketplace. In the outdoor **mercado** of Praia on the island of Santiago, this woman proudly displays her vegetables that are for sale.

8

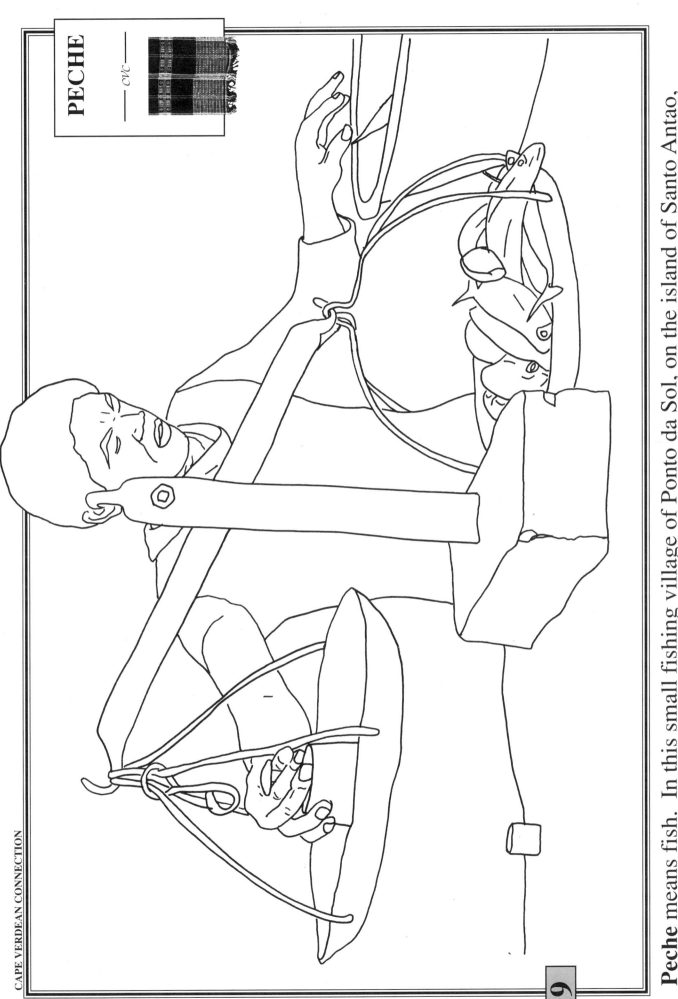

PECHE

cvc

Peche means fish. In this small fishing village of Ponto da Sol, on the island of Santo Antao, **peche** is weighed on a balancing scale and sold near the dock.

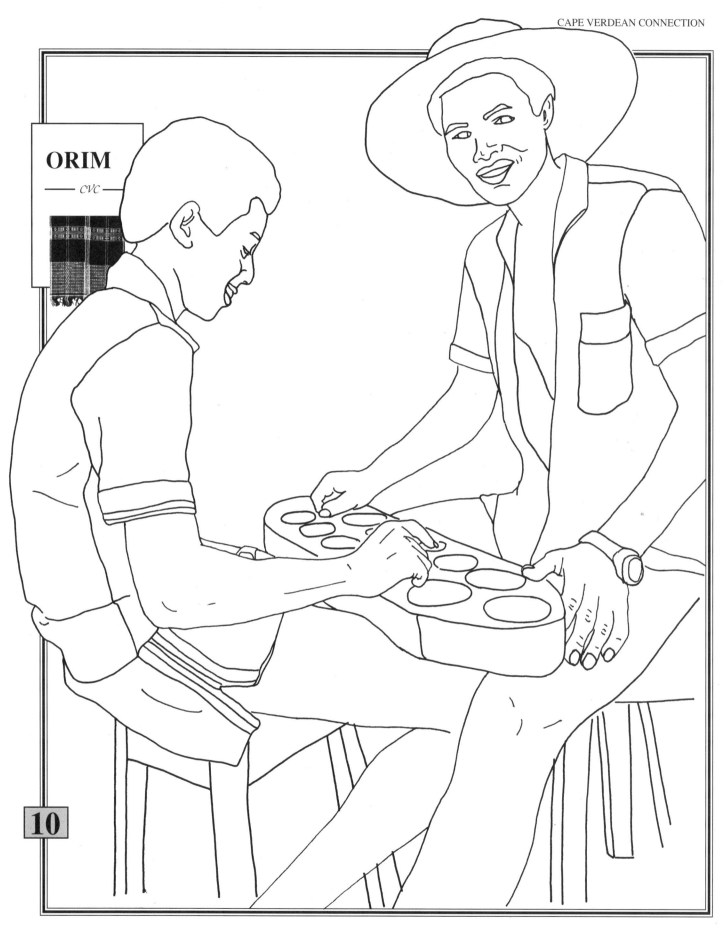

ORIM

— CVC —

10

Orim, is an ancient African game that is enjoyed in all the islands of Cape Verde. **Orim** is played on a wooden board, with grooves carved along both sides. It is played with small stones or beans that are **orim.**

SAL

CVC

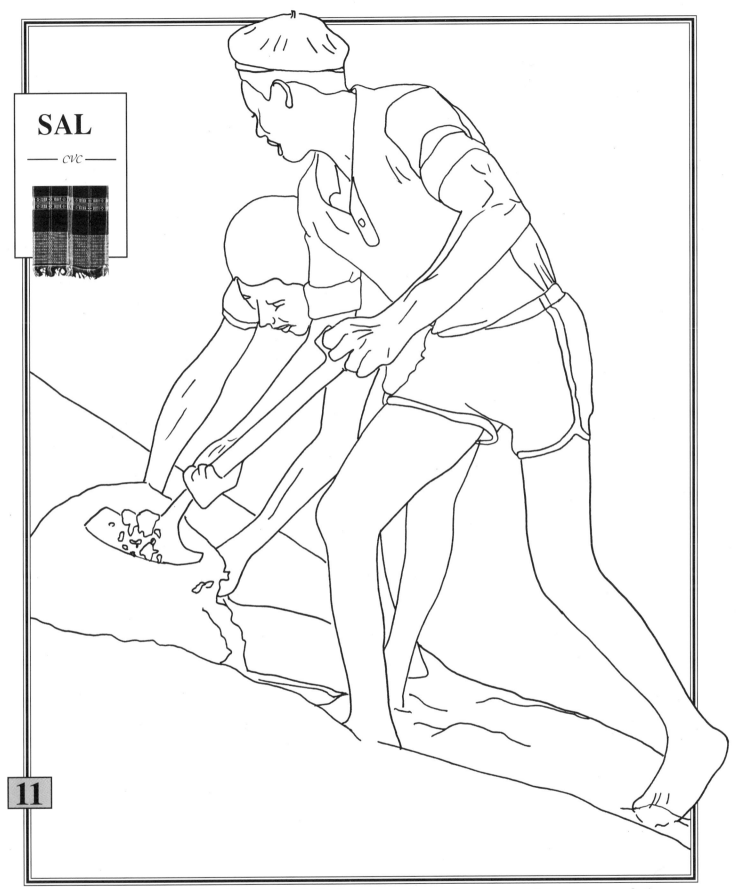

11

Sal, means salt. The island of **Sal**, was given its name because of the amount of sal found there. At one time sal was Cape Verde's leading export.

MORABEZA

—— cvc ——

Morabeza, means welcome. As you arrive in the islands, a warm **morabeza** will be waiting for you from the stewardess of TACV, (Air Transport of Cape Verde).

CASA

—— CVC ——

Casa, means home. Francisco Benhil Silva, a 94 year old retiree, sits in the hallway of his **casa,** enjoying the afternoon in Sal Rei, on the island of Boa Vista.

13

CRIOULO

— *cvc* —

Crioulo is the name of the language that Cape Verdeans commuicate with throughout the islands. However, the official language of Cape Verde is Portuguese, to communicate with the outside world.

14

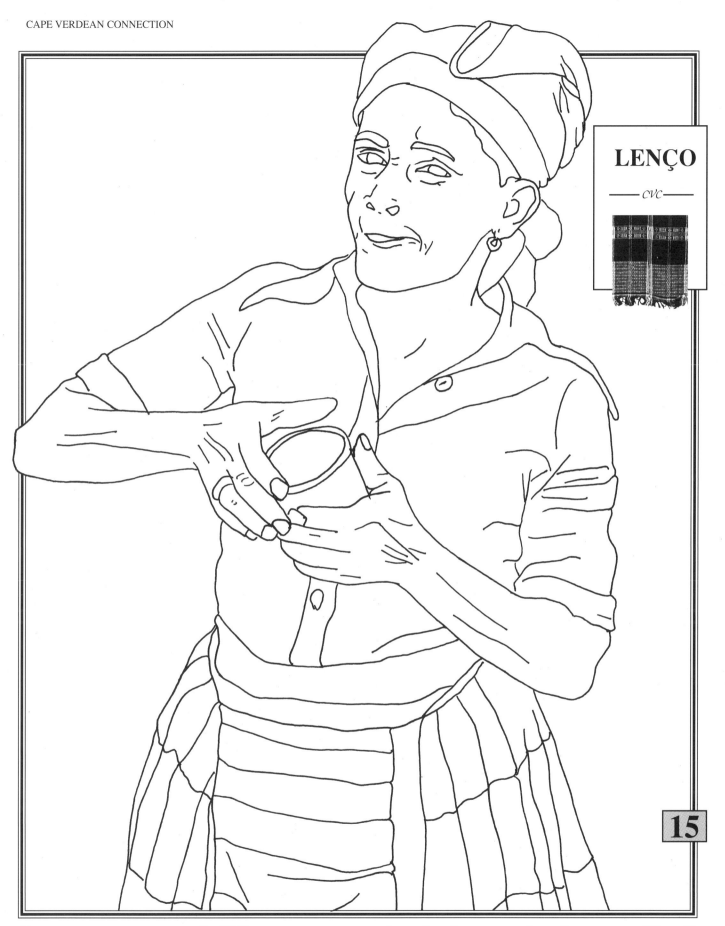

LENÇO

CVC

15

Lenço, means scarf. Where a woman ties the knot on her **lenço,** will tell you what island she comes from. This woman is from the island of Santiago, where white lencos are commonly used.

ARCO

cvc

Arco, means bow. On the island of Sal, this violinist creates mornas on his instrument with the use of an **arco.**

BATUQUE

cvc

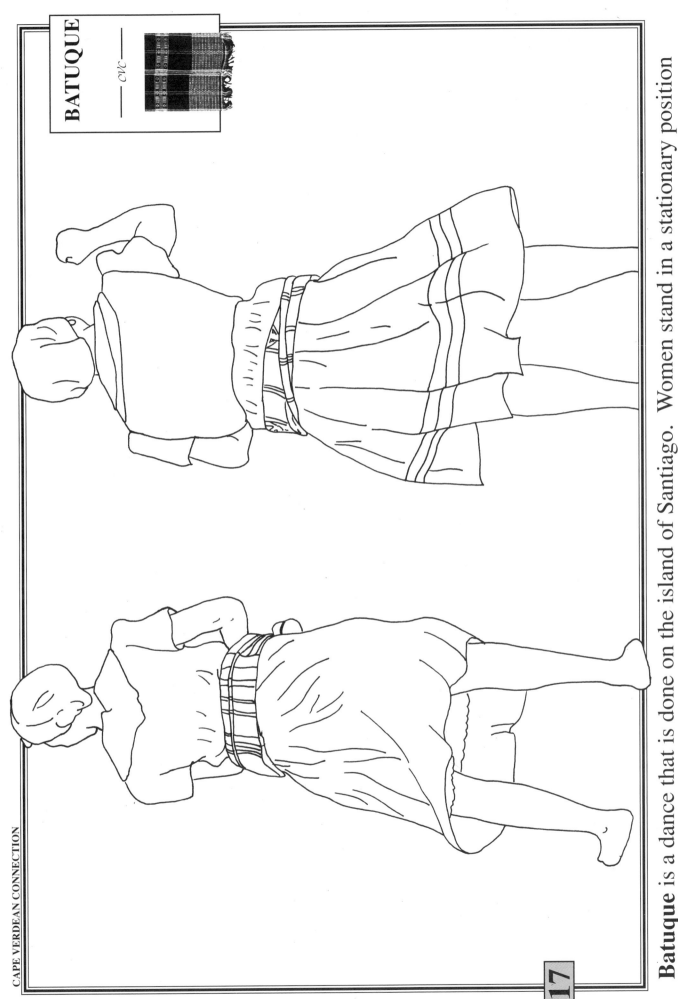

Batuque is a dance that is done on the island of Santiago. Women stand in a stationary position and shake their hips to a beat that is made by pounding a cloth with ones hand.

CARRAGA

— CVC —

Carraga, means carry. On the island of Santo Antao it is common to see young girls, **sta carraga** (carrying) heavy sacks on their heads.

18

LOJA

—— cvc ——

19

Loja, means store. In the village of Joao de Noli, on the island of Brava, you can buy anything from ears of corn, to postage stamps, in **lojas** like this one.

MININO
BAMBUDO
— CVC —

20

Minino Bambudo, means carrying a child on ones back. At the market-place, you can find many **minino bambudo(s)** and women carrying baskets on their head.

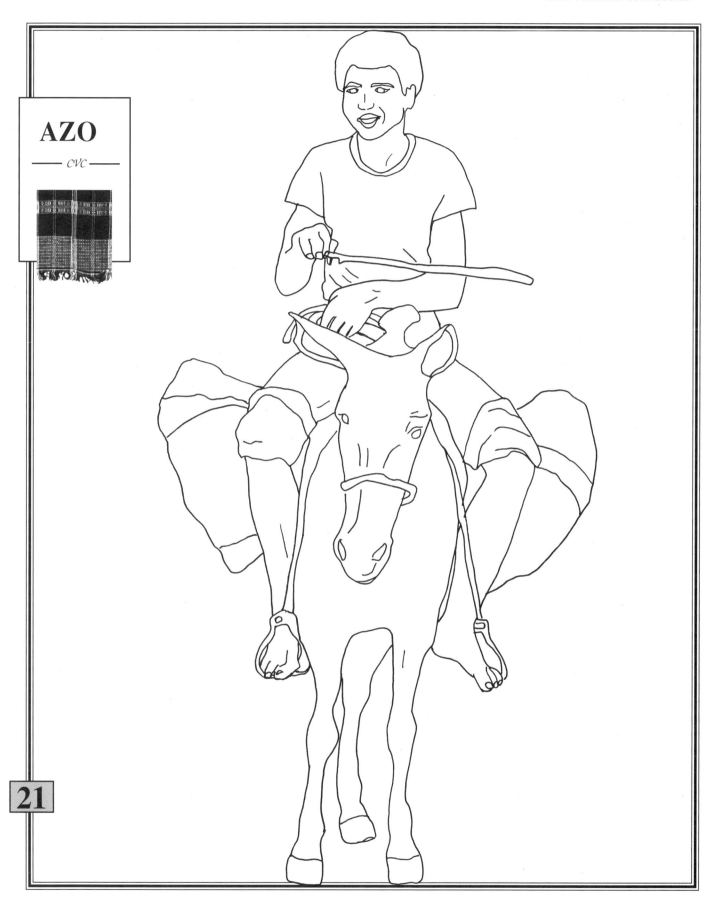

AZO

CVC

Azo means donkey. **Azo(s)** are not only used for transportation, but they are also used to carry many different items. Sometimes, **azos** transport water or wine containers on their backs.

BOTI

cvc

_____ _____

Boti, means boat. Fishing is the occupation of many Cape Verdeans and the upkeep of their **boti** is very important. This fisherman is caulking his fishing barco.

PISCADOR

—— *cvc* ——

Piscador, means fisherman. Inside the tuna cannery at Tarrafal, Sao Nicolau, this **piscador** is mending his fishing nets.

CATCHO DI BANANAS

— *CVC* —

Catcho di bananas, means bunch of bananas. A young girl is carries a **catcho di bananas** from a nearby region. Bananas are one of Cape Verdes' leading exports.

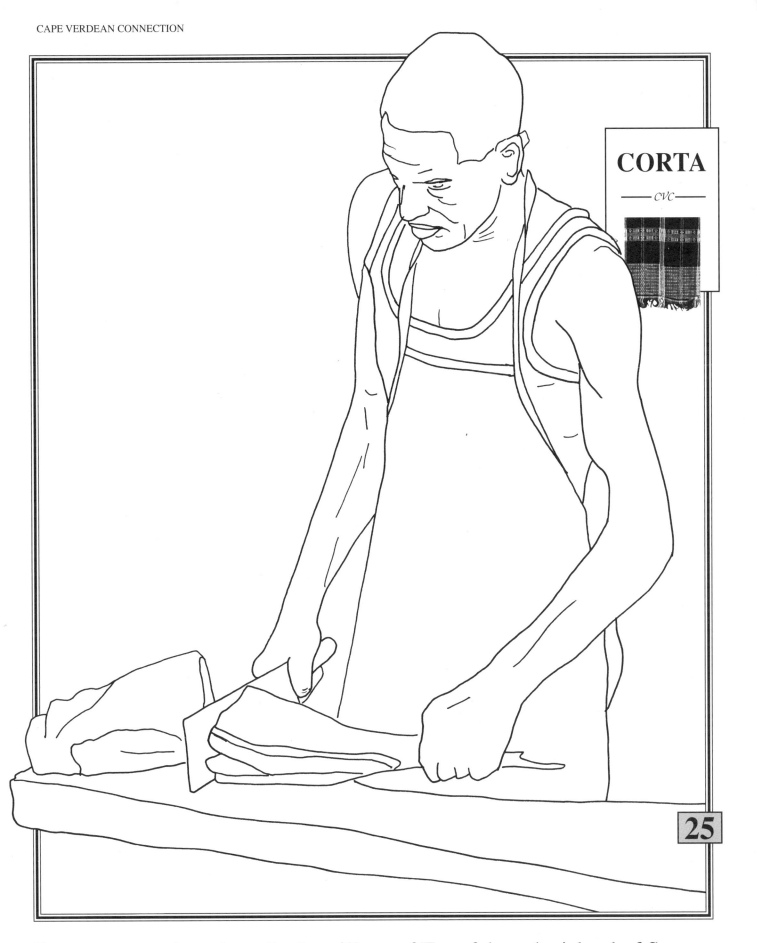

CORTA

— *CVC* —

25

Corta, means chopping. In the village of Tarrafal on the island of Sao Nicolau, this fish cutters **corta** tuna.

FORÇA

— cvc —

Força, means strong. The winds of Cape Verde are **força** and are ideal for windsurfing. The first windsurfing boards appeared on Sal Island between 1984 and 1985.

TCHAPEU

— *cvc* —

27

Tchapeu, means hat. **Tchapeu(s)** are used by dock workers at the port of Praia on the island of Santiago. Cape Verde receives about 3,000 hours of sunlight a year and the average temperature is in the mid 70 degrees range.

ÁGUA
— *cvc* —

28

Água, means water. Recycling has gone on for years in the islands. Yellow containers like this one, originally held cooking oil from Holland, but now it is used to carry **Água.**

LABORATÓRIO

— *CVC* —

Laboratório, means laboratory. Experiments are conducted in this **laboratório** that is located in Praia, the capital of Cape Verde.

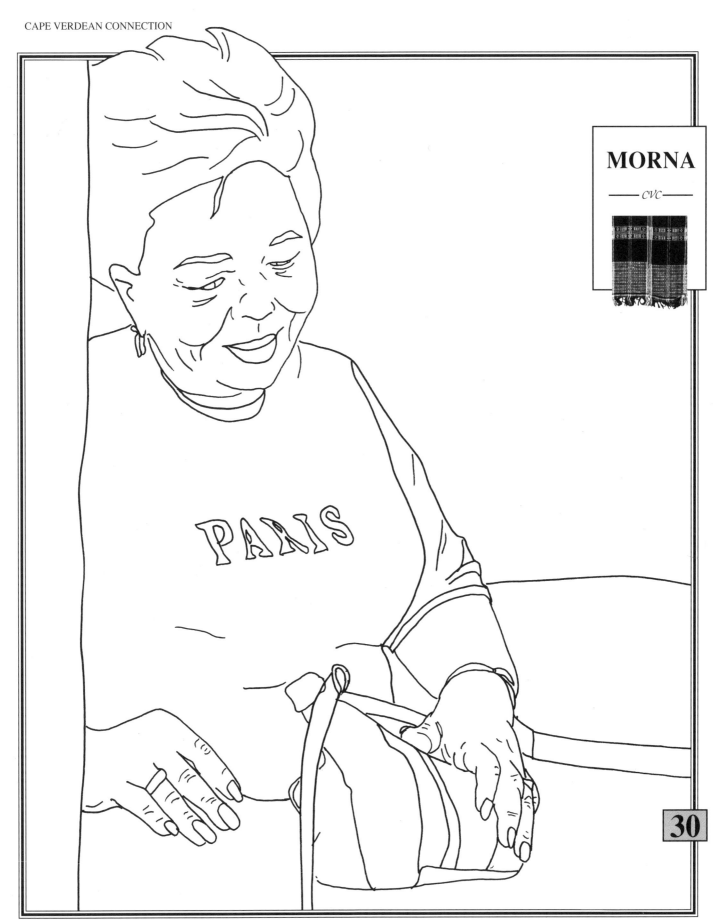

MORNA

CVC

30

Morna, means a Cape Verdean ballad. Cesaria Evora, has been considered by many as the "barefoot diva" queen of the **morna.** She is now an international recording artist on Sony Records.

COLADERA

— *CVC* —

Coladera, is an energetic upbeat type of Cape Verdean music. Bana, one of the islands best known singers, is one of the many singers who were instrumental in making the **coladera** popular in the CVA community.

**TCHAPEU
DI PADJA**
— *CVC* —

Tchapeu di padja, means straw hat. The **tchapeu di padja** this young girl is wearing was made on the island of Boa Vista.